Operatic Arias

Wise Publications
London/New York/Paris/Sydney/
Copenhagen/Madrid

Exclusive Distributors:
Music Sales Limited
8/9 Frith Street, London W1V 5TZ, England.
Music Sales Corporation
225 Park Avenue South,
New York, NY 10003, United States of America.
Music Sales Pty Limited
120 Rothschild Avenue, Rosebery, NSW 2018, Australia.

This book © Copyright 1993 by
Wise Publications
Order No. AM91312
ISBN 0-7119-3563-7

Cover design by Hutton Staniford
Compiled by Peter Evans
Music arranged by Stephen Duro
Music processed by Interactive Sciences Limited, Gloucester

Cover photograph courtesy of London Features International

Music Sales' complete catalogue lists thousands of titles and is free from your local music shop,
or direct from Music Sales Limited. Please send a cheque/postal order for £1.50 for postage to:
Music Sales Limited, Newmarket Road, Bury St. Edmunds, Suffolk IP33 3YB.

Habanera
from Carmen

Composed by Georges Bizet (1838–1875)

The Flower Song

from Carmen

Composed by Georges Bizet (1838–1875)

Moderately

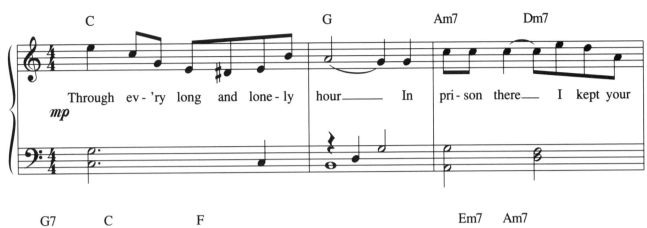

Through ev-'ry long and lone-ly hour____ In pri-son there____ I kept your

flow'r, And though its bloom____ was swift-ly gone____ Its haunt-ing

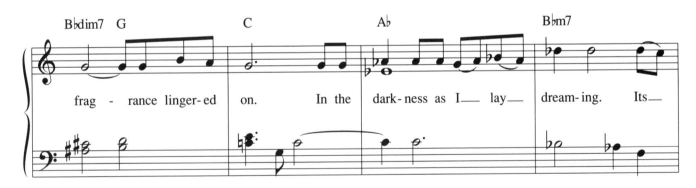

frag - rance linger-ed on. In the dark-ness as I____ lay____ dream-ing. Its____

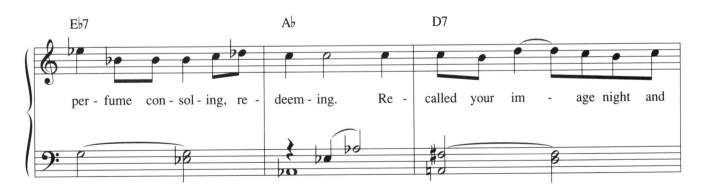

per-fume con-sol-ing, re- deem-ing. Re - called your im - age night and

Toreador's Song
from Carmen

Composed by Georges Bizet (1838–1875)

You Can't Evade The Truth
from Carmen

Composed by Georges Bizet (1838–1875)

Slow

You can't e-vade the truth the cards are say-ing clear-ly, no mat-ter how you try.

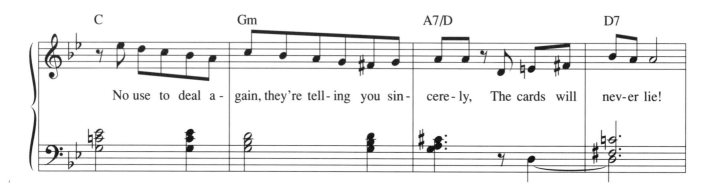

No use to deal a-gain, they're tell-ing you sin-cere-ly, The cards will nev-er lie!

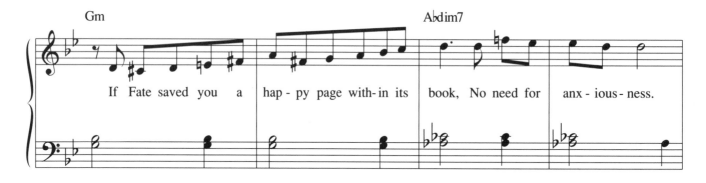

If Fate saved you a hap-py page with-in its book, No need for anx-ious-ness.

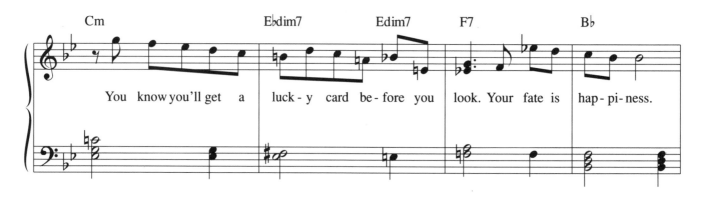

You know you'll get a luck-y card be-fore you look. Your fate is hap-pi-ness.

Serenade
from The Fair Maid Of Perth

Composed by Georges Bizet (1838–1875)

On With The Motley
from I Pagliacci

Composed by Ruggiero Leoncavallo (1858–1919)

The Birdcatcher's Song
from The Magic Flute

Composed by Wolfgang Amadeus Mozart (1756–1791)

Pour, O Love, Sweet Consolation
from The Marriage Of Figaro

Composed by Wolfgang Amadeus Mozart (1756–1791)

die, or, I beg you, let me die. Bring me com-fort in my

suf-f'ring, hear my bro-ken heart-ed sigh!____ Give me back my lord and

hus-band, or, I beg_____ you____ let me

die,____ or____ let me die. Give me back____ my lord and

hus-band, or, I beg____ you, let me die!

I Remember The Starlight

from Tosca

Composed by Giacomo Puccini (1858–1924)

Musetta's Waltz
from La Bohème

Composed by Giacomo Puccini (1858–1924)

And then 'tis mine to mark their hid-den long - ing and all the pas-sion in their eyes

and then the joy of con-quest o - ver - comes me; Ev - 'ry man is my prize!

And thus their hearts, their hearts I cap - tured as if by ma - gic all my own,

Ah, rap - ture! Ah! rap - ture! 'Tis mine a - lone.

D.C. al Coda

Coda

fess but ra - ther die!

25

One Fine Day
from Madam Butterfly

Composed by Giacomo Puccini (1858–1924)

Moderately

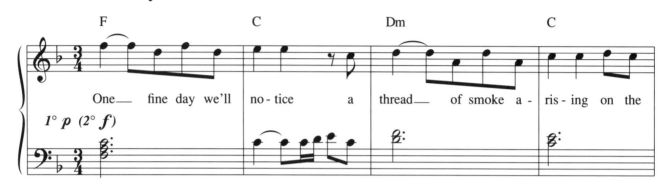

One— fine day we'll no - tice a thread— of smoke a - ris - ing on the

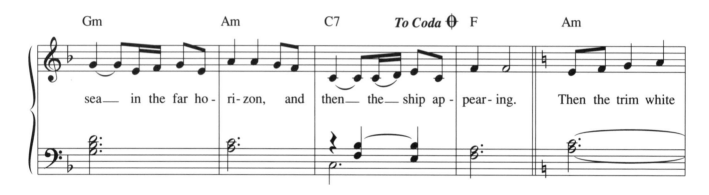

sea— in the far ho - ri - zon, and then— the— ship ap - pear - ing. Then the trim white

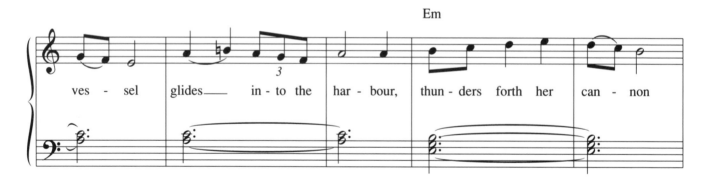

ves - sel glides— in - to the har - bour, thun - ders forth her can - non

See you? Now he is com - ing! I do not go to meet him. Not I! I

Fairest Isle, All Isles Excelling
from King Arthur

Composed by Henry Purcell (1659–1695)

When I Am Laid In Earth
from Dido And Aeneas

Composed by Henry Purcell (1659–1695)

When I Have Often Heard
from The Faery Queen

Composed by Henry Purcell (1659–1695)

With movement

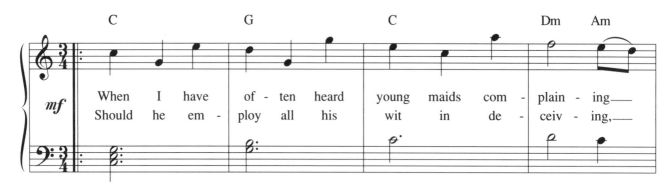

When I have of - ten heard young maids com - plain - ing___
Should he em - ploy all his wit in de - ceiv - ing,___

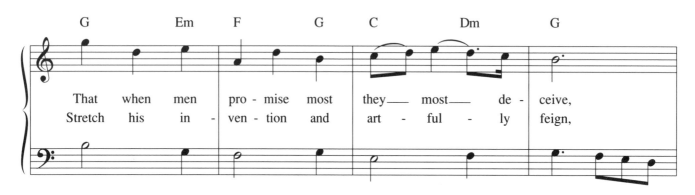

That when men pro - mise most they___ most___ de - ceive,
Stretch his in - ven - tion and art - ful - ly feign,

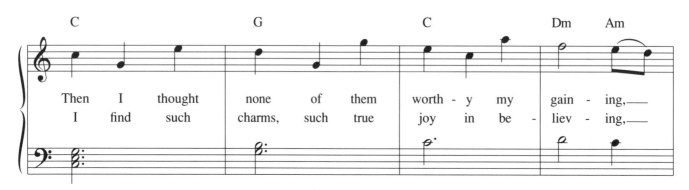

Then I thought none of them worth - y my gain - ing,___
I find such charms, such true joy in be - liev - ing,___

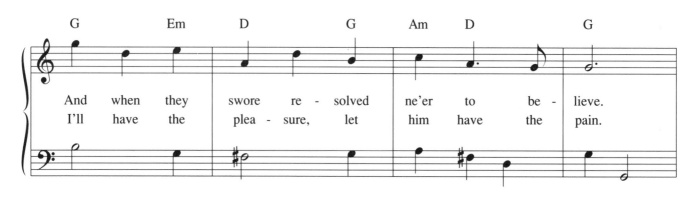

And when they swore re - solved ne'er to be - lieve.
I'll have the plea - sure, let him have the pain.

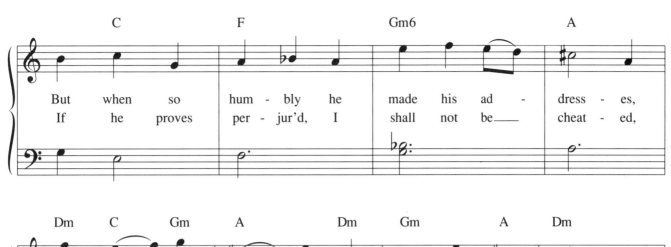

But when so hum - bly he made his ad - dress - es,
If he proves per - jur'd, I shall not be___ cheat - ed,

With looks___ so soft,___ and with lang - uage so kind,
He may___ de - ceive___ him - self, but ne - ver me;

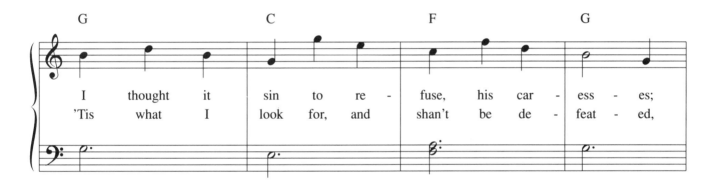

I thought it sin to re - fuse, his car - ess - es;
'Tis what I look for, and shan't be de - feat - ed,

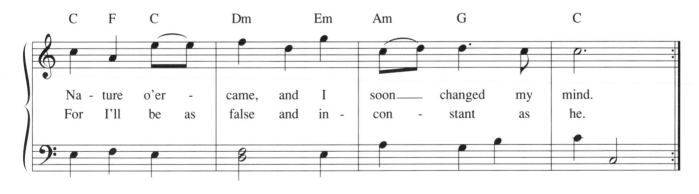

Na - ture o'er - came, and I soon___ changed my mind.
For I'll be as false and in - con - stant as he.

My Heart At Thy Sweet Voice
from Samson And Delilah

Composed by Camille Saint-Saëns (1835–1921)

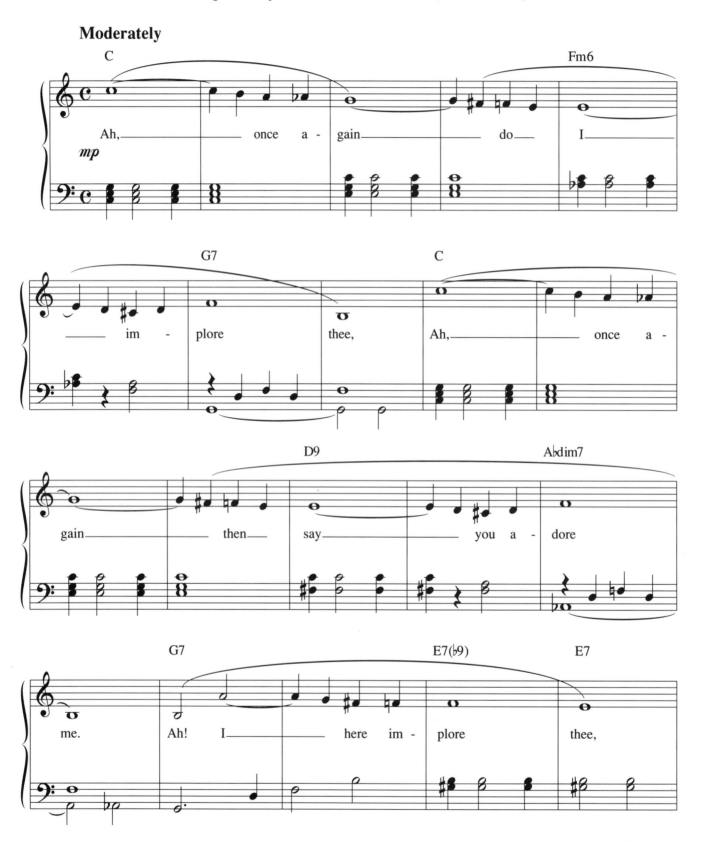

Here Am I In Her Boudoir

from Mignon

Composed by Ambroise Thomas (1811–1896)

La Donna è Mobile
from Rigoletto

Composed by Giuseppe Verdi (1813–1901)

Treasured Mem'ry Of His Name
from Rigoletto

Composed by Giuseppe Verdi (1813–1901)

Moderately

Treas - ured mem - 'ry of his name, Name of him that I a - dore! May its bright and glow - ing

Oh! Star Of Eve
from Tannhäuser

Composed by Richard Wagner (1813–1883)

Oh! Wake Not Yet (Berceuse)

from Jocelyn

Composed by Benjamin Godard (1849–1895)

Moderately

Oh! Wake not yet our dream,

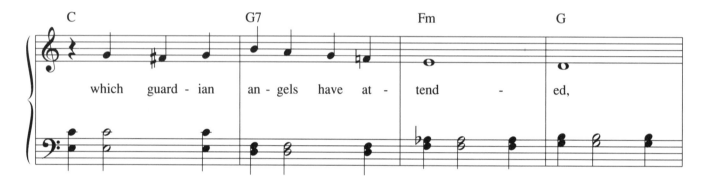

which guard - ian an - gels have at - tend - ed,

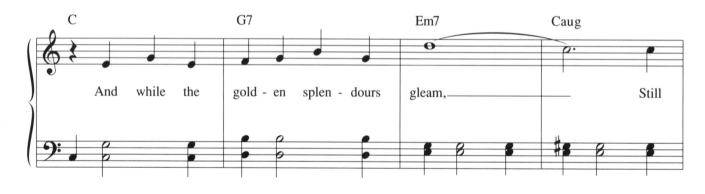

And while the gold - en splen - dours gleam, Still

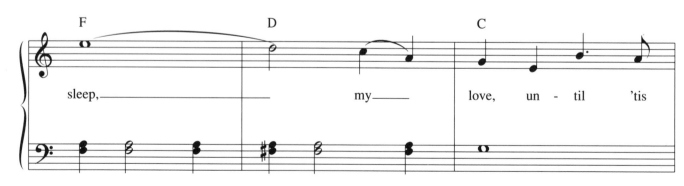

sleep, my love, un - til 'tis

Ah! So Pure

from Martha

Composed by Friedrich von Flotow (1812–1883)

Medium tempo

-vine; Mar - tha, Mar - tha, thou hast left me, My poor

heart has flown with thine, Thou____ of sun - shine hast____ be -

reft me, If thou com - est not a - gain,

Ah! If thou com - est not, death be mine!____